FIRST TIME
PHARMACIST

Richard R. Waithe, PharmD

• • • • • •

EVERYTHING YOU DIDN'T
LEARN IN SCHOOL OR
ON-THE-JOB TRAINING

WWW.RXRADIO.FM

A Dedication

Hey Mom, check it out… I wrote a book. Bet you didn't see that coming. Please don't read it though, it's for new and aspiring pharmacists, not you. However, along with everything that I do, this book was inspired by you. I work hard every day to show that you've raised someone that always strives for a bigger impact and a better world.

I am also appreciative for the content contributions by, Jason Auricchio, Tyler Dalton, Mike DeArmas, and Adam Martin. These fine gentlemen have helped with not only this book, but my journey to helping better the profession of pharmacy. And huge shout out to Mike Corvino and Gary Vaynerchuk. You are the only two people in this world that always makes me feel like I'm not working hard enough. The energy coming from you two is super motivating.

And I can't forget about everyone on social media that helped with content ideas included in the book. The support of the Rx Radio community is truly amazing. Thank you all.

And last but certainly not least, to the best significant other anyone could ever ask for, Laurie, thanks for letting me be me.

Contents

Introduction

Hello there. My name is Dr. Richard Waithe, and I'm a community pharmacist. I began my pharmacy career with Target back in 2011. After leaving Target Pharmacy (now CVS/Pharmacy) I began working for Publix, a chain of large grocery stores in the southeast, US. It was an interesting time for me because over the course of eight months, I was proficient in three completely different pharmacy systems and their respective corporate cultures.

It's now 2018, and with over seven years of community pharmacy experience, I wrote this book to share some of the things I learned that pharmacists don't usually learn in school or in formal on the job training. I hope it will be more like a handbook, or a reference guide if you will. I'll include some personal experiences and lessons learned from them. The book is written in no particular order, so if you're someone who prefers to read sequentially, awesome. But, if you feel like you really want to know how to avoid misfills, feel free to start at Chapter 3, so on and so forth. There are a few topics I asked a few of my good friends to chime in on because I wanted to cover topics that I thought they knew better than I did on it, so they've been kind enough to provide their input.

This book isn't intended to take the place of your formal on the job training or replace your reading of policy and procedures of the pharmacy you work for. Instead, it's intended to help prepare you for things you wouldn't expect or otherwise would not learn until it actually happened to you. The one thing you definitely can't prepare for though is the paper cuts. You're going to have a bunch of those. All jokes aside, I really wanted to gather some experiences and advice over the course of the last seven years and create a supplement to your formal training. I'll cover things like insurance processing, preventing misfills, dealing with difficult patients, and much more. I hope it's truly valuable. To get started, here's three pieces of advice:

1. If you haven't had your first day alone yet, trust your training and take your time. It will be fine.
2. You will never feel ready.
3. You will never know everything.

Disclaimer

None of the information in this book should be taken as legal or financial advice. Make sure to always adhere to state and federal laws when practicing pharmacy. This book is in no way liable for any actions taken from the information contained within.

Chapter 1 – Love

I love pharmacy. But obviously, we all have different interests, and *you* may or may not love pharmacy. I don't think enough people genuinely think about their love for the profession. Now that you're a pharmacist: How do you feel about the profession? What do you love about it? Are you excited for what's to come? Or are you still thinking about doing a residency? Whatever the case may be, the reality is that if you're reading this book you're likely going to be a practicing community pharmacist for the foreseeable future. Let's make that learning priority #1. We'll talk about what to do if this isn't where you want to be in the last chapter.

Chapter 2 – Yourself

You know when you're on a flight, and during the safety video they talk about how you have to put on your oxygen mask before helping others? The situation here is very similar. In this chapter, we'll talk about you and how you should be taking care of yourself and managing your time to ensure a great quality of life.

A Pharmacy is a Business

This paragraph will be referring to large corporation pharmacies. So, if you're going to work for an independent pharmacy you can skip to the next paragraph. Ok, so you're still here meaning you'll be starting your career with one of those large pharmacy chains like CVS or Walgreens. Understand that the pharmacy (or corporation) you work for is a business, as is everything really. This business is pretty much like a living organism. And one thing you have to realize is that, as a living organism, usually a business does not care about you, the individual. The corporate machine has zero feelings for you. I know that's a little harsh. But unfortunately, it's true. Your boss, of even your boss's boss, may love you as a person and as a pharmacist. But if they get pressure from the corporate/business rules or parameters in place, you may have to be disciplined or even terminated in certain situations. It's really important to keep that in mind. Think about this when you're deciding between caring more for your corporation and caring more for your patient. Keep this in mind when you're putting the importance of performance on the job before your own health and wellbeing. Also think about this when making decisions that could affect the integrity of your license. Take care of yourself, and then worry about your team so they can in turn worry about you. Often times, adopting the extreme form of this mindset may not help you move up in your company. Not that it's absolutely impossible, and it's a really sad thing to say, but it's true.

Day to Day

Distractions
So, how does one remain efficient at the pharmacy? We'll talk about prioritizing in a second. Handling workload is usually a very difficult thing to do when first starting out, especially if you constantly have patients at your counter. What also makes it worse is that pharmacists often start off as floaters. So the workload can be completely different from one day to the next.

First thing you really need to do is become proficient at your pharmacy's computer system. Then, you'll have to learn to be comfortable with telling people to give you a second. Working at a pharmacy, you'll deal with tons of distractions. So, when people interrupt you, be friendly (but a little stern) with asking for a second, whether that is with a patient or your technicians. A pharmacist's head is always on a swivel and our ears are always open. We can't help it. But minimizing this and keeping your attention on your task is a must. Be able to acknowledge patients who show up to the counter, but make sure they're not a complete interruption to your task.

Prioritizing
The key to prioritizing your day is to create a workflow system. Here's how I usually prioritize my day:

1. Turn on computers, slightly obvious. =)
2. Check to see if there's any tasks past due in the queues left from the previous day.
3. Check your email or your company's message boards.
4. Check adjudication, prescriptions with insurance or system problems.
5. Check for clinically problematic prescriptions or ones that require a call to a prescriber.

During these steps, I am accounting for any waiters that show up with prescriptions they want immediately. Now, this is just an example illustrating how I do things. I am in no way saying this is the standard. But I think you should figure out what works best for you and your particular pharmacy and have something similarly set up.

I also try to keep an eye out for certain types of prescriptions coming in electronically or via fax. Some pharmacy systems can detect prescriptions that are usually needed sooner, like antibiotics, versus chronic medications, like metformin. These urgent prescriptions would then be set as a priority to be filled. But if it doesn't, you and your techs should try to recognize these and bump them to the top of your queue. These are usually the people to come in and want their prescription ready as soon as possible. The urgent prescriptions include, but are not limited to, antibiotics, prednisone and other oral steroids, acute pain medications like Tylenol #3 or short term prescriptions for things like ibuprofen 800 mg. Making these prescriptions a priority will make the day go by much smoother, i.e. less people screaming at you. Keeping up with patients who are waiting in the pharmacy is also pretty hard. It's so easy to put a prescription in the system and completely forget about it due to constant interruptions. So figure out how good you are at keeping up with waiters. Do you forget about them easily? Do you need to write it down on a sticky note as a reminder? The better you are at keeping up with waiters the better your quality of life on the job will be.

Dealing with Workload Volume

Working for a large community pharmacy can sometimes be luck of the draw. In any given company, there are slow stores and super busy stores. At a slow pharmacy, you'll likely have very little to no tech help, but your counter interactions and prescription count could be low. On the other end, in a super busy pharmacy, your counter interactions and script count will be high, but you'll likely mainly be verifying and answering patients' questions. Dealing with these two completely different demands are very unique, but I think adhering to the above on prioritizing makes managing the workflow much easier.

Work Life balance

At the writing of this book, I work 12 hour days and alternate working every other weekend. Some pharmacies have been changing their schedule to be more like the traditional 8 hour days. But I've yet to experience how that works. Believe it or not, work life balance, in the sense of working versus not working is really not that difficult to achieve. You have a lot of weekdays off to get things done and on every other week, Friday, Saturday, and Sunday can be spent with family and friends. There's 168 hours in a week, so let's say you sleep 8 hours a day and 40 hours of work, you will have a full 72 hours per week for anything else you want to do, given you aren't staying after hours in the pharmacy. If you start coming in to work early or staying 2 hours after close, you will start cutting into that free time. But I'd say it's like any other 9-5 in that aspect. Now if you start taking on extra-curricular activities, like organization involvement or you want to start a side business, it gets tough. I'll discuss that briefly in chapter 5.

How a Pharmacist Fits in Fitness

I'm a firm believer in the importance of staying fit, especially as a healthcare provider, but I'm no expert in physical fitness bringing us to our first guest. Dr. Adam Martin, founder of TheFitPharmacist, is an expert at staying fit while practicing as a full time pharmacist. Take it away, Adam!

"With all of the 30 different tasks we are expected to do all at once as pharmacists, how can we even think of adding one more task to our plate, especially something that requires 30-60 minutes of our time 3-5 days per week?!? Insanity? Unrealistic? Impossible? One may think. But as a pharmacist who has worked full-time in the community setting for close to a decade and having competed in four bodybuilding competitions, I have found some super simple tricks that have enabled myself, and those I work with as a nutrition consultant and personal trainer, to master their management in making fitness a consistent part of their personal wellness script for success.

Here's the key: consistency. But how do you find the time? It's not about living in the gym. In fact, studies repeatedly show that 86% of Americans have no interest in ever going to a gym at all. That's right, *86%!* There's no black and white solution: going to the gym is one option, but it's not a "you have to do it or else." It's about finding some physical activity that you *enjoy*, because if you like doing it, you'll likely *keep* doing it.

Here are some simple solutions that'll best fit in a pharmacist's busy schedule:

1. *The shortest distance between two points is a straight line*

That is, if you're trying to get in a workout after your shift at Club Pharmacy (aka your employer), go STRAIGHT to your workout! Whether it's to the gym, outside for a walk, or lacing up those Silver Sneakers for some laps at the mall, one of the most effective ways to ensuring that happens is to go straight from work to your workout. That may mean packing your workout clothes and gear to take with you to work. You can either change at the pharmacy at the end of your shift or have your gym bag packed in your car so you have everything you'll need for a great workout.

"But I'll just stop at home really quick after work..." No, don't do it.

Have you ever tried that, and sat down to just tie your shoes, and then the reasons for staying put start to flood your mind? For most people, sitting for just two seconds means "game over" for the workout plans. So, stay in the game, stay on your way to make it happen!

2. Proper preparation prevents poor performance

You can't successfully follow through with the first tip if you don't pack your gym bag with all of the essentials to make the workout happen. What do I mean? Well, the *exact* equipment will vary from person to person, but for 99% of us, use the following gym bag checklist to ensure you are packed for peak performance:

- Workout clothes: shorts, shirt, jacket/sweats if cold
- Water bottle
- Headphones
- Music with a great beat
- Post workout snack/protein
- Digital watch/stopwatch
- Jump rope
- Lifting gloves/wrist wraps/straps if desired
- Shaker cup/mixing bottle
- Small towel – you DO plan on sweating it out, yes?!

3. If it's important to you, you'll make it happen; if not, you'll make an excuse.

Here's a fun fact: we all have the same amount of willpower. That is, it's a limited resource that weans off as the day goes on. With that being said, if you know that you'll be using up a lot before the end of the day, and you just can't find it in you to get a workout in after work, make hitting your workout first thing in the morning a priority. This is a great way to get your blood flowing, set you up for success for the rest of the day, and you will feel super accomplished knowing that your workout is already in the books before the sun has finished rising. Nothing can stop you now!

4.   No coffee, no workee-out-ee.

Of all of the hundreds and thousands of shimmery, fancy pre-workout supplements on the market today, one beats them all and is backed by repeatedly proven scientific studies touting its effectiveness: caffeine. Of course, if you have certain medical conditions or are taking certain medications, you should avoid this and always consult your physician before starting ANY supplement of any kind (but you already know this, fellow pharmacist). Devoid of any contraindications, this will add some serious focus and energy to your workout to enable you to reap the maximum benefits from your commitment to excellence. It's not a "must", but it sure does fuel the fire for fitness!

5.   Utilize the buddy system.

Studies have shown over and over again that of the people who have successfully developed the habit of working out consistently, many have reported having an account-ability/workout partner. Decades of research still names this one trait as one of the most common success habit of those who follow through on their workout plans. This keeps people on track with physical fitness programs for many reasons, but psychology is the strong driving force here: we all have days (yes, even me) when we just don't feel like working out. But if our spouse, neighbor, or friend is counting on us to show up, we will grin and bear it to keep our word to our workout partner. Buddy up, giddy up, and go!

6. *Optimize your time.*

If you are trying to get in a really solid, complete workout and incorporate weight lifting, cardio, and vary your intensity, but find that doing all of those things separately is just not realistic with your time, say hello to combination magic! There are several workout regimens, gyms, and clubs that combine these and more into one 30 or 60-minute workout for maximum efficiency. Orange Theory Fitness and Cross Fit are just two examples, but this is yet another option you can use to make the magic happen and fit it into your schedule! Bonus: if you decide to join one of these clubs, get there early to meet those in your class, and boom, you just added in one of the above tips and gained an accountability partner (or two or more). Look at you combining steps!

By prioritizing your health and wellness, you'll begin to allow your body to perform at 100% its potential. It will allow you to provide the very best care possible to those you serve and interact with in your daily life. This belief is the core of what it means to be a FitPharmacist, and the whole reason I created TheFitPharmacist movement. That is to help each other through the obstacles we face as pharmacists, to inspire each other and support each other in reaching our own optimal health as healthcare professionals so that we can better optimize the health of those we serve. To join the movement and for more free resources to help simplify living as a FitPharmacist in mind, body and spirit, visit our community at:

https://thefitpharmacist.com."

Thank you so much Adam! That was some amazing info and make sure to follow him on Instagram @TheFitPharmacist.

So, we've learned about work life balance, how to make sure we stay fit, but wait a second, where are we even going to live?

Finding a Place to Live

One of the motivating factors for keeping up my motivation during school, especially undergrad, was that I was finally going to have my own nice place in beautiful Miami, FL. I couldn't wait to get my first few pay checks so I could have enough money for a few months' rent. But when I had that money in the bank, and I was ready to move out of my mom's house, I had no idea what was in store for me. So, in order to help prepare you for this possible situation, you'll now read some advice from a good friend of mine and real estate professional, Mike DeArmas. Hey Mike! All yours!

"Hello pharmacists! First of all, congrats! You've made it through school and you are ready to embark on this journey we call a "career." And if you're still a student, don't worry, it'll be over sooner than you think. Now, there is one fairly important decision you still need to consider: "Where are you going to live?" As a real estate professional, I am constantly bombarded with questions regarding the housing market and what are the best options for those seeking a new home. While these questions are very specific, I am going to give you some solid advice that will assist you in what is destined to be a vital decision for you moving forward.

1. Finding Your Realtor

If you choose to seek the advice of a realtor, be advised, they're not all as helpful, honest, and just plain awesome, like yours truly. Just messing with you. But in all seriousness, there are some bad characters out there, so choose wisely. The first "red flag" when dealing with a realtor is when the realtor is constantly rushing you. This is a major decision, if the realtor cannot understand that you need some time to make a decision, then perhaps they don't deserve your business. The next indicator that this realtor isn't for you is if he/she is constantly ignoring your budget and trying to get you to spend more than you are comfortable with. The truth is, we get paid off commission and that commission is usually tied to the sale price. So the more you spend, the more he/she makes on that sale. Lastly, if the realtor puts a limit on how many homes they will show you, do yourself a favor, run away! There are many consummate professionals in the real estate industry, but there are some duds. Get a feel for yours and if they are not treating you right, find someone that will.

2. Renting vs Buying

Let me preface this all by saying that real estate is a fluid market and that any and all decisions should be made with the advice of a trustworthy real estate associate. The first question to consider is whether to rent or to buy. Renting will be tempting due to less upfront costs and the flexibility, but since the market changed after the real estate boom, the month to month cost is virtually the same as paying a mortgage. The issue with renting is that you are essentially paying someone else's mortgage and you are not using your housing situation as an opportunity. Renting is a great option for those who cannot come up with the funds for a down payment on a home, those of us with some questionable credit issues (although many landlords request to run your credit as part of the application process), and those of us that want the flexibility to move around if they so choose.

3. Buying a Home can Make you Money

I purchased my first home when I was 25 and I am admitting my bias towards purchasing, but hear me out. I am a major fan of capitalizing on opportunities and making money as often as I can. We all need to have a home somewhere, why not make money off that fact? The truth is, when you rent, you are guaranteed a 0% return on that investment. When rents were considerably cheaper than mortgages, I understood why some people would go that route, but since rents have sky-rocketed, I do not understand how anyone that has the means to own a home chooses to rent. Making a smart purchase could result in a short-term or long-term gain financially. I have many clients who purchase a larger home than they really need and charge a friend rent to stay with them and cover most of their mortgage. I've had other clients who have purchased a home, lived in the home for years and then when their salary grew they purchased a new home and began utilizing the initial home as an income property. Most of my clients have purchased a home, lived in the home while the value grew, and then sold that home to be able to purchase the home they really want.

Other Considerations
However, no matter what you decide, there is no wrong way to handle this. The best advice I can give you is to ensure you do your due-diligence and at the very least, have a conversation with a realtor. The good news is that the seller pays the realtors so his/her advice is completely free of charge! Markets are constantly changing and you need to have the most up to date information in order to make a solid decision. There are many factors to consider including: commute, Home Owner's Association (HOA) fees, parking fees (yes, some places charge you for parking), maintenance of the property, pet restrictions, application fees, taxes, hazard insurance, flood insurance, renter's insurance, etc. It can get extremely over-whelming, but being able to discuss these factors with someone knowledgeable is invaluable.

If you want to get in touch with me, shoot me an email at MikeDeArmas@yahoo.com or connect with me on LinkedIn.

Happy hunting and best of luck!"

Mike DeArmas
Licensed Real Estate Professional

Hey guys, it's me Richard again. Hope you got some good value out of that! I sure did, anyway, last but not least, what about nutrition?

Nutrition

I'm saving the best for last, nutrition. I could have been the one to give you my thoughts on it, but, this is another one of those areas where I wanted to bring in an expert. I wanted you to hear from a pharmacist that's really passionate about the topic. Introducing Dr. Tyler Dalton, a community pharmacist that is passionate about nutrition and helping his patients take care of themselves by watching what they eat. Overcoming a digestive health issue himself, he knows firsthand the importance of it all. Take it over, Tyler!

"As students, most of your events were centered on free food. Whether it is from study groups, your favorite organization's monthly meeting, or whatever speaker provided the next free meal. If your school was anything like mine, most meetings consisted of pizza, and lots of it. Now that you are no longer a student, you're *"making that pharmacy money"* and you should be able afford to make healthier choices and choose to put better food into your body.
Now that you aren't spending 10–15 hours a day at school, you can take back your life, and most importantly your health!

It's time to make your health a priority.
As you enter into this next phase of life, make a commitment to yourself and to your health. Focusing on

improving your nutrition will not only make you feel better and provide more energy, but it will also set an example for your peers and patients. After all, you are a healthcare professional. You learned all the brand/generics, you learned about drug interactions and maybe even some food-drug interactions. But, one thing you most likely did not learn about is nutrition and wellness. Here are a few basics I've learned along the way.

1. Mindset is everything

Do not allow yourself to fall into the *"busy trap"* or victim mindset- that you work in a crazy store with no time for a break. This kind of thinking is *rubbish*. Your body needs a break, no matter how mentally tough you think you are or how much your supervisor/manager might pressure you. Starting your very first day, make it a precedent that you will take a break. You have to take care of yourself first, your health, and your mental bandwidth. You can only verify so many prescriptions without taking a break or at least catching your breath. That being said, take care of yourself and don't let a busy schedule be an EXCUSE for you to eat garbage, or worse, not eat at all.

2. Never Skip Breakfast

Despite what you have been told growing up, there is no scientific evidence to support breakfast as being the most important meal of the day. But, before stepping into a busy day in the pharmacy, you do want to make sure you have some food on your stomach.

Instead of following the traditional norm of rushing around in a whirlwind in the morning, take a few minutes, collect your thoughts and fill your body with some nourishing foods. Make sure you stock up on a balanced breakfast consisting of fiber, protein and fats to keep you full. Here

17

are some good examples below:
- Eggs + Avocado & Salsa
- Overnight oats (milk, chia/ flax seeds, fresh fruit)
- Greek yogurt + almond butter

3. *Always be prepared*

By having snacks around the house or at the pharmacy, you always know you have something healthy to fall back on when you get a craving. Especially when you are running late and feel like you don't have time to pack a meal. When I first started working, I found myself mindlessly eating or running out to the front of the store to grab a bag of chips or candy. Most of these not so good decisions were made because I failed to plan. Remember to keep it simple, and have small meals to eat throughout the day.

Here are some of my favorite snacks to keep around:
- Protein Bar
- Yogurt
- Fruit (apples, bananas, blueberries, strawberries)
- Old fashioned rolled oats
- Hummus + veggies (carrots/celery)
- Organic peanut/almond butter
- Non-GMO Organic Popcorn
- Healthy Nuts: almonds, walnuts, pecans

4. *Batch/Meal Prepping*

You've seen your friends post about meal prepping on Instagram, now it's time for you to consider doing it too. Figure out what day works best for you, and prepare a few meals for the week. This will make your life way easier in the long run and lessen the burden of deciding what to eat every day. Plus, you will save money and your body from eating fast food all the time. Focus your meal prepping around simple to prepare foods, e.g., crockpot chicken and veggies, soup, and salads. Something that you can prepare in a short period of time and that will keep fresh throughout your work week.

5. Stay Hydrated

Always drink water, every day. You've probably heard the phrase "drink eight 8-ounce cups of water a day." This is easy to remember and a good general rule of thumb. The truth is, there isn't an exact number you should drink on a daily basis, but some sources recommend anywhere from 8–15 cups of water a day. Even when you are not thirsty, you should be continually drinking water to make sure your body is hydrated. Your body cannot distinguish between your sense of thirst versus your sense of hunger. So next time you're hungry, drink a glass of water and wait a few minutes to determine if you're actually hungry or if your body was just craving some hydration.

6. Energy Drinks

Since pharmacists have energy demanding jobs, you may find yourself needing a good go-to source of energy. Which option is best? Easy. Real, fresh brewed coffee. If you know Dr. Waithe, you'll know he approves of this! Stay away from energy drinks like Monster and Red Bull since they're full of artificial chemicals and sweeteners. Coffee provides a purer and easy to process form of energy.

Take Home Message:
Take care of yourself! There is always time for a lunch break, even in retail. Communicate with your team and let them know you are taking an uninterrupted break, even if it is just for 5 minutes. That time will allow you to collect your thoughts without feeling pressured to respond to the phone ringing, drive through beeping or someone popping into the patient consultation window.

Work with your staff to create a monthly pot luck event. This breaks up the burden of doing all the cooking yourself and makes it fun. That way, everyone has something to bring to the table and keeps you from potentially eating the same boring food every day.

Setting an Example
In school, we were told time and time again, diet and exercise are first line therapy for most disease states, especially cardiovascular. But let's turn the table, by becoming examples for other healthcare professionals and our patients, we can better engage with them and empower them to live healthy lives.

Is it ok to have a cheat day, mess up every now and then? Yes of course, we're not robots and not expected to eat perfectly 100% of the time. The important thing is that we set a good example. Imagine for a second you have a newly diagnosed Type 2 diabetic coming in. You're fully aware nutrition is going to be something you'll stress. But how can you authentically and with a good conscience talk to them about its importance if just a few minutes ago you slugged back an extra-large cola, waffle fries and a heart-attack burger? Better yet, imagine if the patient sees you eating that or drinking a large sugary drink as they walk past you. They might think to themselves, "well if my pharmacist does it, it must be ok."

Any time you slightly downplay or say "it's not that bad" then patients are more likely to take that as a crutch and sometimes take it a step further. Wear your white coat proudly, be an example. Pharmacists have been trusted members of the community for decades. Keep that level of respect and allow your patients to talk to you about nutrition, eating healthy and maybe the idea of actually making lifestyle changes to reduce their medication burden. What's more powerful is if you've personally struggled with a certain disease state like diabetes, hypertension, or heartburn, and through lifestyle changes have overcome your condition. There is nothing more powerful or encouraging to others than a personal journey to health. I myself suffered from horrible heartburn for years and was on a PPI for 5 or 6 years. I knew my heartburn was mostly related to poor diet and lack of exercise. After graduation from pharmacy school, I decided to get serious about my health; I changed my diet dramatically and was able to stop taking my PPI almost immediately. So now when I counsel a patient coming to pick up medication for heartburn, I can talk to them with much more conviction about the importance of lifestyle changes, reducing the need for medication and unnecessary risk from taking a PPI/H2 blocker long term. If they know their pharmacist can do it, they'll have better confidence knowing they can too!"

Financials

What are your first steps financially? For student loans, do you make the minimum payment or try to pay off early? Is getting a financial advisor really necessary? These were questions asked by aspiring pharmacist, Jennifer Ryder, and is probably the most unifying questions from new pharmacists across the country. Now that you'll be making that "Pharmacy money," there are a few things to keep in mind in order to manage your finances. Our next expert panelist, Jason Auricchio, is a financial advisor, here to drop some knowledge bombs. Jason, you have the floor!

"Hello healthcare professionals. There are common financial concerns most pharmacists face after graduating and I hope to make you a little more comfortable in dealing with them.

Student Loans: Paying Off Debt Vs Building Wealth
This is probably the top concern I see with graduating healthcare professionals. 'Should I pay off my loans as quickly as possible? Or should I pay the minimums and just pay them forever?' The reality is, it doesn't have to be an either-or decision. You can have a plan to pay off your loans without putting every single extra dollar of disposable income towards paying them off. Most of your federal loans will even offer you an income-based repayment plan with a "loan forgiveness option" at the end of 10, 15, or 20 years. Although you do have to pay taxes on the portion of the loan that is forgiven, this can be a great option for someone wanting to save for short and mid-term goals while paying down their debt.

What it really boils down to is this: Do you prefer to have a greater sense of financial security by getting your student loans down to zero as quickly as possible? Or would you rather pay them down at a slightly slower pace while having savings that you can use when emergencies or investment opportunities arise? Regardless of your answer, you should work with a financial advisor to ensure that your strategy aligns with your goals.

Group Benefits: What is it and which one is right for me?
As the name implies, group benefits are when a group of people can benefit from the same policy. This is usually provided to you by your employer at their expense or at a cheaper 'group' rate. Although cheaper does not always mean better, group benefits can be a great foundation for your financial planning. You should consult your HR department and/or a financial advisor to understand whether buying into a group benefits program could compliment your family's situation.

Here's what I'd do:
- Contribute money to a 401k/403b retirement plan up to the amount that your employer will match (typically 3% or 5% of your salary).
- Enroll in short-term disability, especially women. Group short-term disability plans are the only plans that pay a portion of your salary when on 'normal maternity leave.'
- Enroll in long-term disability and pay the tax if you can. This is because, when an employer fully pays for the cost of the long-term disability benefits, any benefits you receive during a claim would be taxable to you. However, if you pay the taxes,

which are generally $5-$10 per paycheck, any benefits you receive would be income tax free.

Supplemental Benefits to Purchase
A good financial advisor will review your entire current financial picture and future goals to determine what products and services, also known as supplemental benefits, are in the marketplace to assist you in reaching your goals. These services can be purchased on your own, outside of your employer's group benefits. While everyone's situation is different, some popular solutions include additional long-term disability to protect your income, brokerage or managed money accounts that will begin to grow your savings, and life insurance, which can protect your current or future family.

Everyone's situation is different and no two plans are alike. It is important to have an advisor you can trust, who will look at your situation and offer justifiable recommendations that will help you obtain your personal, professional and financial goals."

Thanks Jason! We appreciate your advice. As you can see, finances can be confusing and flat-out overwhelming. If you think the above high-level overview was daunting, you may want to consider talking with a financial advisor. Or, you may want to take the time yourself to do some serious research and figure it all out on your own. It doesn't matter which route you choose to go with, but definitely pick one so that you know you are making the best financial decisions. Ok, now back to our regularly scheduled programming.

Now that you've got what you need to take care of yourself, we can begin to consider others. Next chapter we'll talk about the pharmacy, your day to day activities, inventory, and dealing with insurance companies.

Chapter 3 – Pharmacy

Most pharmacies provide a decent training program you can follow. Especially because you have a few weeks that you spend as a grad pharmacist, since you're not yet licensed, working under the supervision of a licensed pharmacist. But even during this time there are tons of things you don't learn. I hope this chapter will inform you of some day to day nuances to better prepare you for when you're off on your own.

Workflow

If you've had any experience in a pharmacy, you can skip down to the next paragraph titled "Inventory Management." If you don't have any pharmacy experience this is an important section. I wanted to briefly provide you with a high level overview of processing a prescription. Being able to understand the process with a bird's eye view helps tremendously with workflow. The following can vary slightly in order, depending on your pharmacy's system but overall the concepts are universal.

Here's the process in six steps
1. Patient drops off prescription (or it comes in electronically, faxed, or phoned in).
2. Prescription is then scanned into system.
3. The information on that prescription is then transcribed into the pharmacy's system. This is the

information that will go on the patients label and what will be recorded in their profile.

4. The prescription then gets processed through both the pharmacies internal prescription processing parameters and gets processed through the patient's insurance to determine payment.
5. After any issues discovered in step 4 are dealt with, the prescription then gets filled. This is where we put the pills in the bottle.
6. The prescription is then verified by a pharmacist to ensure the information was transcribed correctly and that the right medicine is going to be delivered to the right patient.

Inventory Management

One thing pharmacy schools don't do a good job at is preparing us for the business aspects of working in a pharmacy. And when your business involves selling products (in our case medications), understanding inventtory management is a must. When running a pharmacy, which is a business, the goal is to be profitable, aside from the whole providing care thing, of course. Your pharmacy will need to make money to keep operating. And one way to ensure the business stays profitable is to manage your inventory. Why? Well, the medications sitting on your shelf i.e. inventory in this case, costs money. And when that inventory does not sell, you've got dollars just sitting on your shelf. Those dollars represented by those medications in the pharmacy are dollars that isn't in the bank or being used for other things like payroll or other operating expenses. As a result, the goal with managing inventory is to attain an equilibrium where you're constantly trying to have sufficient inventory on the shelf to serve the needs of your patients, but not storing too much inventory where you have medications sitting on the shelf for prolonged periods of time. Now that you've got the concept of inventory management down, let's go over some best practices for inventory management.

Most pharmacy systems have ways to set something called "order points." Order points in the case of a pharmacy, for a specific medication is some maximum/minimum range of on-hand inventory that marks a threshold of when to order more and how much to order. These order points can be changed based on the pharmacy's needs. Let's jump into an example: Say a pharmacy sells 10 bottles of metformin every month. Your pharmacy system will have a set specific minimum and maximum number (order points) of how many metformin bottles to have on hand in the pharmacy. Because your pharmacy sells 10 bottles, the minimum can be set at three and the maximum to be set at 10. With these order points set in place, when your metformin inventory gets down to three bottles, it will then need seven more bottles to meet your business needs of 10 bottles a month. This is the ideal situation for inventory management. You'll never have more bottles of metformin than you need, yet you'll have enough on the shelf to fill your patient's prescriptions when they need them.

Our example with metformin is a case of managing a high volume, low priced item. But managing inventory is also important with low volume, high priced items. This brings us to our next example, this time with the pricey medication: Linzess. Due to the price, you'll likely not want to have more than one bottle sitting on the shelf, let alone 10 bottles like we did with the metformin. Because again, having three bottles of Linzess could be a few hundred dollars you could be using for other operating expenses. As you can see, finding the balance between not keeping unused high price medications on the shelf while making sure your patient's monthly needs are met leads to proper inventory management which can ultimately result in a profitable business.

A Lesson in Refrigeration.

I want to share a fun story that happened to me where I got to learn a valuable lesson in refrigeration inventory management. I once closed my pharmacy and left the refrigerator door cracked. I came back to the pharmacy the next morning with a huge puddle of water right below the fridge, and thought to myself, "Hmm, that's weird." As I inspect further, I see the door still cracked and all the medications being stored in there were at room temperature since the previous night. Finally putting it all together I screamed to myself, "%@#&." Seems like the ice from the freezer melted, resulting in the puddle of water. For some reason I thought, "let me call the manufacturer to ask them what to do." I really didn't want to damage out the entire inventory in the refrigerator. I found out the manufacturers will sometimes have data to determine something called excursion times. Excursion times are instances where a medication is exposed to a temperature outside their recommended range. And manufactures run studies on their high cost medications to have data available in case there is a break in the recommended storage requirements during transportation. But these times can also be utilized in the community setting in the case of my situation. I was able to find out the specific time frame the medications I had in the refrigerator could be at room temperature and be safely put back in the refrigerator and it would still be suitable for consumption. This information is usually only kept in-house and I was only able to find accurate data after calling the manufacturer directly. However, there were some medications that didn't have that data available, which I did have to damage out. But, lessons learned here are; 1) always make sure your fridge is closed tight and 2) call the manufacturer if you need information on excursion times.

Oh, but that wasn't my first altercation with a refrigerator. I once opened the pharmacy one morning to see one of the refrigerators wasn't even on! At some point in time during the previous day there was a short in the circuit. The fridge was fine, but something happened with the socket that it was plugged into. Back on the phone with manufacturers I went. Lesson here is that that stuff happens, but make sure to check your fridge temps right after opening and right before you leave the pharmacy.

Bonus Tip
Sometimes, I won't even fill high priced items until a patient shows up. Opening a stock bottle often makes that particular medication not returnable. So if you open a bottle and fill a prescription and that patient doesn't come to pick it up, you'll be stuck with that medication, whereas if you never opened it you could usually return it to your distributor. Same thing goes with putting a label on an expensive cream. Usually your distributer won't accept a returned medication that appears damaged, and peeling off a label that doesn't cleanly come off often "damages" that product, making it un-returnable.

Mistakes and Misfills

I think pharmacy school does a really good job at talking to students about misfills and how it's about processes and not people. They really drill it into you that when a mistake does happen that we should not blame anyone, and avoid punishing the individual, but instead focus on the process. They do this to facilitate the bettering of processes and discourage people from hiding their mistakes. And while this is true and the right way to approach misfills, it doesn't take away from the fact that you can be disciplined for a mistake in the pharmacy. It also doesn't take away the fact that you'll feel absolutely distraught if you do it. And it's one of those things you'll never truly know that feeling until it happens to you. It hurts. It's one of the worst feelings to have as a pharmacist, and unfortunately it will likely happen to you.

When you make a mistake, you'll be really hard on yourself. You'll begin to doubt everything. Sometimes even your ability to be a pharmacist. Panic and anxiety sometimes set in. The feeling in your gut that ensues is just so unexplainable. I need you to be fully aware and expect these emotions. But I also want you to realize that mistakes are going to happen. It happens to the best pharmacists I know. The most important thing to do after noticing a mistake is to ensure your patient is safe. Whether it is the wrong medication that went out or the wrong dose, call the patient *immediately*. You don't have to admit to anything, but take this time to confirm the suspected mistake and guide them on directions on minimizing injury. You could always say "we're just double checking something." After the mistake has been confirmed, then follow your pharmacy's policy and procedure for handling it. Some pharmacies require certain verbiage when communicating a misfill to a patient so ensure you are aware of any of those that may exist for your company.

Avoiding Mistakes

Your first six months as a new pharmacist is when I think you're the most vulnerable to making mistakes. It's when you're learning your groove and cadence. The first six months can be the most stressful time because you're just getting used to it all. What I've learned over time is that while as a pharmacist, we feel like we're double checking everything carefully, however, over time, through the course of a day, you end up just going through the motions. My experience has taught me there are some things that make me stop and say, "OK, there could easily be a mistake here, let's really double check this." I've compiled a list of those situations that make me take an extra look. Most of the scenarios on this list have actually been misfills I've seen, or for the very least near misses:

- Vitamin D2 versus D3 – Make sure you're picking the right one, memorize or always look up ergocalciferol vs cholecalciferol
- Prozac versus Paxil – These are two brand name SSRIs that can easily be confused for each other.
- Package sizes – Filling a prescription for the wrong quantity is usually considered a misfill, and often times this can happen with creams and ointments. Sometimes you're supposed to dispense a 60-gram tube it gets filled using the 30-gram tube and you didn't catch it.
- Cream versus ointments versus gels – While safety isn't really a concern here, these are just one of

those things that'll you'd beat yourself up for because you didn't catch it.

- Metoprolol Succinate versus Tartrate – As you know, there are two types of metoprolol. One is extended release and one is immediate release. A lot of misfills happen here because of the wrong dosage form being dispensed. Make sure to take that extra look with metoprolol to determine if you're supposed to be dispensing the succinate or the tartrate. Oh, if it doesn't specify on the script, call!

- Levothyroxine versus Synthroid – Patients taking a thyroid supplement usually need to stay on either the brand or the generic. They aren't usually interchangeable like most drugs. While filling one and not the other is generally not considered a misfill unless it is specified brand medical necessary on the hard copy. If this is the case, you'll have some pretty irate patients if you give them the wrong one. I usually take a peek at the patient's profile to see what they've gotten in the past whenever I'm verifying a prescription for thyroid replacement.

- Amoxicillin, Augmentin, and Azithromycin – I know this should be something easy to catch. But I've seen people make mistakes here. And it could be a costly one, imagine you have a script for azithromycin since your patient has a true penicillin allergy. But, that allergy isn't listed in the patient's profile and you accidentally fill an amoxicillin, which could be a fatal misfill.

- Warfarin – Warfarin is an awesome medication. We have an antidote for it and we can monitor how well, or how well it's not working. But, if used improperly it can be deadly. Please give Warfarin special attention when you're verifying it. Giving too high of a dose or too little can have very different results, but both can be fatal.

- Haldol versus Nadolol- This is just a simple look alike sound alike combination of medications. You'll see other examples in your practice and you'll pick up on which ones to look out for.

- Ophthalmic versus Otic – Special attention should be given to eye and ear drop prescriptions. These are very easy to get mixed up and cause a misfill.

- Nifedipines – There are so many different types, so make sure you're dispensing the one intended by the prescriber.

- Birth Controls – It feels like there's enough birth control combinations as there are all other medications combined. And a lot of them have very small nuances that make them different. Some have iron (Fe), some have 21 days of active ingredients and some have 28 days. And similar to thyroid replacement, women usually want to stick to the same brand of birth control. When verifying a birth control prescription, I'll also take a look at their profile to make sure the brand she's getting is the one she usually gets.

- Lovenox – Dealing with Lovenox prescriptions can be tricky. Figuring out the appropriate quantify to dispense and how much to inject can be confusing. Make sure units of measurement are clear on the prescription's sig; you don't want them injecting the wrong dose.

- Effexor versus Effexor ER – As with every medication that also comes with immediate and extended release dosage forms, in my experience, these two have been quite the common source of misfills.

- Zofran versus Zofran ODT – Same as above, medications with these different dosage forms can be a source of misfills.
- Capsule versus Tablet – This is another one where safety is usually not an issue with this type of error. A lot of pharmacists interchangeably fill either of them. However, dispensing a capsule instead of a tablet can usually be considered a misfill. This can become problematic if your employer has a threshold of amount of misfills before you may be disciplined. So, always a good thing to double check.

Again, this list isn't comprehensive, but it's just based on my experiences. And your pharmacy may consider some of the above scenarios misfills, or it may not. I'm confident that based on your experiences or even your patient population you'll see different trends. One really good way to prevent mistakes is to show patients the medications they're about to take home with them. You'd be surprised at the amount of mistakes I've caught doing this. Plus, it also prevents headaches of patients going home with a medication they didn't want because their physician told them to stop taking it. Sometimes they'll call you and be super upset because when they got home they realized they received a medication they didn't want. Or worse, maybe that patient won't realize they're taking the lisinopril that was supposed to be cancelled since they switched to losartan, for instance. This now goes from an inconvenience to a safety issue.

One thing that's not pleasant about showing patient's their medications one by one at pick up is that it can take time. With patients on one or two medications, it may seem like it can be done quickly, but when your patient is on five, even eight medications, it can begin to feel like a very time consuming process. But to me, it's worth it. In some pharmacies, it's policy to show patients the exact medications they're taking by taking the bottles out of the bags at pickup. But, for some companies, there is no mention of this in their policy and procedures manual. Some people think it's a good idea to say the medications out loud, but I never do that unless the patient asks me out loud, "what am I getting today." I'd rather show it to them to protect their privacy and follow HIPAA laws.

Here's some other general advice I have in addition to the above examples for habits to prevent misfills.

- Papers and HIPAA – a lot of times your pharmacy will be printing multiple papers for different people on the same printer. Make sure when you're dealing with more than one paper you look through each page to make sure you're not mixing someone else's personal health information with someone else's. This can be a potential HIPAA violation; some companies see these as being equivalent to a misfill.
- Bagging – In addition to the tip above, bagging medications will be a thing of the past when pharmacies move to a paperless system. But until then, make sure to look at everything twice before you place it into a bag. So before you place any vial or piece of paper, double check the name of the

patient on the paper matches the name on the bag, if your system is set up that way.

- When you feel rushed, you should be checking more, not less.

- If you're working without a technician or rushing to get a waiter's medication filled, try not to complete the entire process in one shot. A lot of mistakes happen because you verify the accuracy of a prescription immediately after you type it, making it difficult to catch your own mistake. After typing a prescription, try to do something else to reset your mind. This will allow you to verify that prescription with some fresh eyes to minimize errors.

- The benefits of keeping a clean workbench are underrated. Stress to your team the importance of a clean and organized workbench and its effect on safety. One way to keep a clean filling area is to make sure your team only fills one patient at a time. In addition, make sure to only scan one bottle at a time. The whole filling thing may be a thing of the past, see next chapter, but scanning one bottle and then immediately filling that particular prescription is important. Most pharmacies have moved to this method of prescription processing so I'm hoping it's clear what I mean by this. And after you or your team fills a script, put that bottle away and back on the shelf. Get it away from the area to prevent filling errors.

- When you and you team are putting a prescription label on a box or stock bottle, it is important not to cover up the NDCs. NDCs on these packages are the best way the verifying pharmacist ensures the right drug is going to the right patient.

As you can see, some misfills can be harmless. But it's everything that comes after it happens that can be tough. The reporting sucks, patients can get very upset at you and your team; you may lose a patient's trust over something minor, or worse, a there is harm to the patient. But ugh, even the small ones can be tough to deal with; it's the confidence in yourself that you lose that can be the worst of it. And when mistakes happen, people will want to blame the employer, work conditions, and distractions; but in reality, you're still going to feel the same way. The bottom-line is this: be careful, because depending on the severity for the misfill, it can stick with you for a few hours to the rest of your life. With that being said, mistakes happen to the best pharmacists out there, so don't be too hard on yourself.

"If you question it, call on it. Whether it is a dosing, frequency, or duration question, call the prescriber to clarify if you question it for a second."
– Brandon Gerleman, PharmD

How many mistakes are too many? Well, technically one misfill can be considered as one too many because it can be fatal. But if you find yourself having multiple mistakes per month or more than three per quarter, I'd say you'd want to really analyze your verifying behavior and start seeking advice beyond this book on how to be better at verifying prescriptions.

Protecting your License

Speaking of misfills, should you get liability insurance? In general, I would say yes for two reasons. First of all, having the peace of mind is so worth it. And second, some pharmacies say you're covered under their general malpractice insurance. But I've also read in some policy and procedures that they'll only cover you once they determine you weren't negligent or something, so that to me doesn't seem very comforting. The hope is that you'll never have to need it, but having it is fairly comforting. However, it is expensive. You can spend $500-$1000 per year for a policy. But, before purchasing a policy, thoroughly review your pharmacy's policy and procedures manual to get a better idea on whether or not it's a good idea for you.

Insurance/Third Party Issues

The two hardest things about managing the day to day operations of a pharmacy is dealing with insurance and managing people. As indicated by the title of this section, here's my shot at giving you as much as I know about basics of dealing with insurance companies.

There are a few pieces of information that you'll need to run a medication through someone's insurance. The most important thing you'll need is the Rx BIN (Banking Identification Number). The second most important thing you'll need is an identification number. Then, sometimes optional, you'll need an Rx group number and a PCN (Processor Control Number) in order for you to accurately process a patient's insurance.

It's important to also understand why insurance would reject a prescription in the first place. Plain and simple, they're a business; and any harm to the patient negatively affects their business. So not only do they need to manage the cost they're paying for patient's medications, they also need to ensure patient's safety. So if a prescription gets billed to them, and it is costly, you may see a rejection. Or if the prescription you process is an unusually high dose or seems like a duplication of therapy, you may also get a rejection. These are just examples, but there's a bunch of particular safety reasons or formulary reasons an insurance company could deny a claim. It'll then be up to you, or your technicians, to trouble shoot the situation. Sometimes you can handle this within your own system, but sometimes you'll have to call the insurance company for help.

Briefly, here are some of the other reasons an insurance company won't pay for a patient's medication:

- Too soon – if a patient picks up a medication and that medication should last them 90 days, but they come back in 60 days, the insurance will reject that prescription basically saying, "hey you just got this, you shouldn't need it for another 30 days"
- Available over the counter – Some insurance companies won't cover medications that are available over the counter
- Cheaper alternatives available – Prescribers love to give patients brand name medications with coupons they got form the manufacturer. The problem is these coupons usually require insurance coverage, and a lot of time they don't cover it since there are cheaper options on the market.
- Mail order preferred – Some insurance companies will prefer their beneficiaries receive their medications in the mail as opposed to a traditional brick and mortar store that you may be working at.

- Non FDA approved treatment – Some prescribers prescribe medications not yet approved by the FDA, insurances sometimes won't cover these medications.
- Non-preferred pharmacy – Your pharmacy may not be the patient's network.
- Non-payment – I've unfortunately had to deliver the news that a patient's insurance company won't pay for their medication because they have missed a payment on their premium.
- Date of service – This rejection happens when you processed a prescription on a previous date than when the insurance would actually approve it.
- Most pharmacy systems have a spot for you to put in prior authorizations, and they're family standard to your specific company so get familiar with those early on.

For some of these rejections, the patient's insurance company may provide the option to complete a prior authorization (PA). PAs can be a frustrating experience for both the pharmacy and the patient because sometimes it can take days, or even weeks for them to be completed. Plus, just explaining this to a patient could be a challenge. Here's how I usually explain it:

"Mr. Carter, unfortunately your prescription requires a prior authorization, have you ever heard of that before? No? Well, a PA is a fancy word for your insurance company wanting more information from your prescriber as to why they're prescribing a specific medication. This will usually happen because of a (include here why you suspect it's a PA e.g., high dosage, duplicate therapy, etc.). These are required to be completed by your prescriber before they'll cover a specific medication. I'll go ahead and send the paper work now to get this process started. But here's how it works. Here's the process:

- We'll send a form to your prescriber's office which they fill out, then send to the insurance company.
- The insurance company will then approve or deny to cover your medication based on the information provided and will provide your prescriber with a decision

We'll let you know if we hear back, in the meantime, if you'd like to follow up on the process you can contact your prescriber or insurance company."

Medicare Part B

The most common Medicare Part B claims you'll usually deal with in a community pharmacy are with nebulizer solutions, diabetes testing supplies, and certain immunizations. These items usually get billed to Medicare Part B, not to their prescription drug plan, aka Part D. Sometimes Part D will pick it up, but usually if you run it through Part D, you'll get a rejection stating something along the lines of "bill Medicare Part B."

There are certain standards the prescription must have but one of the most important things usually missing is the diagnosis code. You cannot bill through Medicare Part B unless you have a diagnosis code, unless it's a vaccine. I won't talk about the rest of the Medicare Part B standards in case these standards are changed, but please refer to your company for specific Medicare Part B requirements.

Coupon Cards

Many patients who are uninsured or just looking for the best deal on a prescription medication will attempt to use a third party discount card to help pay for their medications. However, pharmacies have been opposed to accepting coupon cards as a form of payment. There used to be widespread use, but there are many pharmacies no longer accepting coupon cards to help patients pay for their medications. This is because these third party coupon cards usually charge the pharmacy a transaction fee, often cutting into the pharmacy's profit. Coupon card awareness has been on the rise due to aggressive marketing by companies like GoodRx. They're also starting to take different forms; some allow you to pay upfront through their app or online website. Patients could then take the card to the pharmacy and then the copay would be $0 since payment was already taken care of on the backend with the coupon card. But again, some pharmacies are not accepting these types of payments anymore due to its negative effect on operations.

In terms of manufacturer specific coupon cards, these are usually run in association with a patient's insurance plan. Your system will be set up to where you can process the patient's insurance first, then the manufacturer's coupon card after. These cards can be tricky because there's always some fine print that includes the following:

1. Maximum coverage – These cards always have a maximum they'll pay. This is where things get confusing for patients because the card may say something like "pay no more than $10 for your medication." But on the back it says maximum card

will take off is $50, for instance. But if the patient's copay is $75, that means the card will only take off $50, and then the patient's copay will be $25. This usually comes as a surprise to the patient, because they are expecting to only pay $10, so you'll often find yourself explaining the situation to them. This situation is made worse if the patient doesn't have insurance or if the insurance doesn't cover it. In this situation, the coupon card will then only take off $50 off the retail price of the medication, often hundreds of dollars. So telling a patient she has to pay $450 when their coupon card says pay no more than $10 can be frustrating.

2. The other fine print included is that coupon cards cannot be used with patients receiving medications by the government, like Medicare, Medicaid, or Tricare.

I do hope you're now much more comfortable with day to day operations and troubleshooting common problematic scenarios.

In the next couple chapters, we'll being to discuss relationships with people. Being a healthcare provider means it's highly likely that the people we interact with on a daily basis are sick, or just not feeling well. Not only are they dealing with all the other struggles of life, they're also seeing you because they need a medication for themselves or someone else. Your patient picking up their metformin prescription may have just received the news of a new diagnosis of diabetes. So the next time you have a problematic patient, or even a colleague that seems like he/she is acting like a jerk, don't take it personal. Yes, sometimes that person just sucks, I get it. But try to think about what they may be going through. Their interaction with you may have nothing to do with you, but it may have been something that affected them six hours ago. I always try to keep this in mind and it's really helped me cope with the times I have rough interactions with other people at work. Hopefully it could do the same for you.

Chapter 4 – Your Team

In this chapter, we're going to talk about your relationships with people, both with your technicians and patients. There are many books out there with theories on the best ways to manage people, so I won't go into much detail on management/leadership techniques. Plus, I think we are all leaders in our own different way, so what works for me may not work for you. I will say though, an important thing to understand about leading others is that the people you lead are very different and respond differently to different types of leadership styles. So trying to understand your team and what they respond to best is very important. However, I don't think anyone responds well with being led by fear, aggression, or disrespect. So definitely don't try leading with those tactics, no matter how bad your day is going.

Your Technicians

Pharmacy Technicians are often times the heart of a pharmacy. They're some of the most undervalued, underpaid members of the healthcare team. Mid to high volume pharmacies would barely survive the day without their technicians. Entire days or even weeks can be thrown off if one technician calls out. What's worse is that the role of a pharmacy technician is not a very attractive position in today's landscape. Most pharmacies are not offering full time positions with benefits. In addition, work conditions are made difficult from increased workload from the result of large retail chains cutting hours left and right. But your technicians keep everything in the pharmacy flowing. So treat them well and always show appreciation for their contributions to the daily workload.

I actually think pharmacists should be working for our technicians. We should start to view them as our colleagues and not our subordinates. I also think it's the pharmacist duty to not allow pharmacy technician to be a victim of verbal abuse by patients or even other pharmacists. Some technicians may feel that their place is to take that kind of abuse, but that should not be the case; rather it should be the responsibility of the pharmacist. You should be the one to step in and diffuse those situations and anything else you can think of that makes it easier for them, you should do that too. After all, they're usually the heart of the pharmacy, so your quality of life depends on it.

My strategy for building relationships with my technicians is to first just get to know them. This is the logical thing to do considering that I will be working with them for so long. Think about it, especially if you're in a mid to high volume pharmacy you'll literally be spending entire days with them on a weekly basis. Likely even more than you'll see your family, given you work full time.

You'll be working super close with them, sometimes in harsh, busy situations. Look for a way to increase moral. At my pharmacy, I created the It Could Be Worse (ICBW) Card. It's literally just a piece of paper with the four letters written on it, "ICBW." We pass this card around the pharmacy to team members who are having a rough day at work as a friendly reminder that, you know…ICBW. The smiles and joy this card has brought to our pharmacy is priceless. I also heard of one pharmacist bringing in a small figurine to the pharmacy and the team member that finds this figurine then gets to hide it, and the fun continues.

How do you work with a technician that's older than you? First of all, if they're older and have a lot of pharmacy experience that means this isn't their first rodeo and they likely understand the dynamic of the pharmacist-technician relationship. So I'd just lead them with respect, really the same way you'd also lead a technician who's younger than you. The key here is to realize everyone is human and has had different experiences, no matter their age. Once everyone understands their roles, and you realize again, you should be working for them, leading a team of technicians, whether they are older or younger should really take the same approach.

Intern to Pharmacist at the Same Store

Oftentimes people who plan to work in community pharmacy end up becoming the pharmacist at a store where they have either interned at or worked as a technician. So one particular challenge in this situation is the transition of going from being almost an "equal" as a tech, to becoming the pharmacist or the "boss," so to speak. I've actually been in this exact situation. Doing two executive internships with my hometown Target Pharmacy (Now CVS Pharmacy), I ended up being the pharmacist where I completed one of those internships. But what I noticed really worked for me was, nothing changed. So that's actually the advice I would give in this situation.

I think becoming the leader of your former team shouldn't change much, at least with your direct relationship with the members of the team. Yes, now you're the pharmacist, and you have a lot more responsibility, but in terms of leading that particular team, nothing should really change. You and the team will start to realize what changes you think would be best for your style, but mostly, if you've been working there you've already identified these issues with workflow and have addressed them. I know saying "do nothing" may seem like an inadequate answer in this particular situation, but it's really my best advice.

Pharmacist-Intern Relationship

If you have been gifted with the opportunity to have a pharmacist intern work at your store, PLEASE don't take this lightly. Pharmacists who have interns have an awesome opportunity. You literally have the ability to shape the future. You can help mold and develop this new pharmacist into the way things should be. You can show them all the wrong things a great pharmacist shouldn't be doing. You can instill in them that everything is always about the patient. What we shouldn't be doing with our interns is treating them like an extra technician. They should be trained to be our mini-pharmacists, not our mini-techs. Plus, if you do a good enough job at training, your interns will be able to take a lot of the workload off of your hands.

"Learn to develop soft skills and people skills. Without knowing how to effectively work with different people, pharmacists can't make much of a difference." – Cynthia Leung, PharmD

Chapter 5 – Your Patients

Perception is Everything

One important way to build great relationships with your patients is to have an influence on their perception. Both their perception of control and their perception of time are very important and we actually have the ability to control that. What I'm about to talk about usually occurs when patients are dropping off a new prescription or they're on the phone asking when they can pick up their prescription. Although what I'll discuss here are minor details, these small interactions can add up and really have an impact on patient's satisfaction. And have you ever heard the saying, "Happy wife, happy life?" Well, there's a similar saying in pharmacy that also rings true and that's, "Happy patient, happy pharmacy team." I know it doesn't sound as cool, but seriously, the happier and satisfied your patients are, the better your job will be.

Perception of Control
Letting people feel like they're in control is empowering. I think it can have a really positive impact on a patient's experience at a pharmacy and their overall satisfaction with you and your pharmacy as a whole. An easy way to influence their perception of control is by giving them the ability to tell us when they're going to pick up their medication.

For example, when a patient is dropping off a new prescription, you should ask them, "When would you like to pick this up?" This may seem a little awkward at first. And some patients may sometimes even look at you weird. But the reason why I love this question is because some people don't want their prescriptions immediately. Some people want to come back tomorrow, or over the weekend even. If you tell them right away, "we can have your medication in 30 minutes," they'll say to themselves, "hmm, really wanted to come back tomorrow, but now I have to wait here." Do you see how that poses some friction? Not only could you have taken the time on that prescription and put other daily activities in front of it, you've also now put the patient in a situation where they may be doing something they didn't want to do. After you ask them when they'd like to pick up the medication, often they'll say, "as soon as possible." Now you have the opportunity to tell them what your wait time is. This minor tweak to these interactions can have a positive impact on a patient's perception of control and which will lead to happier patients.

Perception of Time
Did you know pharmacists can bend time? Well, technically we can bend the perception of time. Let me explain. One of the very first lessons I try to teach community new comers is the importance of a patient's perception of time. But how?

So you followed my advice above and the patient said they want to wait for their prescription. And you work at a big box retailer, so you tell the patient. "it'll be ready in 30 minutes." So they go off on their merry way to look around the store. To your surprise, the patient comes back in 20

52

minutes and asks, "is it ready?" You say, "no, it's not." You then look at the time and see it's only been 20 minutes. But what you don't know is that patient felt like it was 30 minutes, heck, they may have even felt like 40 minutes has gone by. See, you never provided them a reference time. That patient may not even have a watch on, so they've returned not based on actual time, but on perceived time. What you should do instead is begin to tell patients a specific pick up time. This eliminates all uncertainty on who felt what. If you tell a patient, "your medication will be ready by 3:30," they'll then pay attention to the time. They can shop all they want, but if they come back before 3:30, they'll know they are early. There wouldn't be any confusion if it "felt" long. This small tweak, in addition to proving the feeling of control, is a recipe for a happy patient.

I really want to reiterate the importance of a happy patient. The happier they are the better things will go for your day to day interactions with them. This is so important because undoubtedly things will always go wrong in the pharmacy. There are so many ways something can go wrong with someone's prescription, and that's when having a great relationship with your patient comes in handy. If you have a wonderful relationship with Ms. Johnson, the one day your entire order for the day is delayed or the medication is on backorder, she won't be mad at you. Or at least she may not give you a hard time. But if you've never had a sincere conversation with Mrs. Johnson, and your interactions with her have always been dry, the day her medication doesn't come in, you may get an earful of it. In addition to influencing a patient's perception, there are many other ways we can better our relationships with our patients, so let's get into those next.

How to Build Great Relationships

Connect with them.
One of the best ways to better your relationship with your patient is to connect with them on something outside of the medication they're picking up. Ask your patients open ended questions to see if you guys have something in common. Ask things like, "How was your weekend Mr. Gomez?" You may find out Mr. Gomez was able to catch up on the recent episodes of Top Chef he had on DVR, and you LOVE Top Chef. Or maybe he answered by telling you about the recent NBA Playoff game that you also got to watch. Try and remember these interactions with your patients you see on a regular basis so you can recall it the next time you see them. These small connections, and your ability to remember them, will go a long way in developing relationships with your patients.

Show Empathy
Demonstrating empathy in any and all situations in the pharmacy is another great way to build relationships with people. The pharmacy school I went to had a class that focused pretty heavily on how to properly express empathy. And that class was super helpful, but a lot of the empathetic exercise we did in class was not real, because it really was just a class exercise. But one thing I learned is that you can't fake genuine empathy. In the real world, people can feel if that empathy is not genuine or not coming from a good place. You can memorize the common empathy phrases like "It sounds like you're very upset," but I think you really need to figure out ways to get to a place where you really mean it.

But it's not only those reflective statements that are important, sometimes it's the delivery of certain messages. For example, I recently had a patient who had what appeared to have a herpes flare up on her lip. She said she had tried everything to get rid of it, even the common over the counter regimen, Abreva. She asked for my advice on what it could be. I could have said, "Ma'am maybe you have herpes." But a more thoughtful response, which is what I gave, was that she may need a prescription because she may have an infection on her lip. It's technically saying the same thing, but the tone and delivery was in a way that made her feel comfortable.

Anticipation

Your ability to be two steps ahead of a patient during a conversation involving an issue with their prescription will be in direct relationship with how good your relationship would be. Being 2-steps ahead means providing the patient with information on what you did to help with the situation or what their options are due to the issue. This usually comes with experience, but I'll provide a couple examples that you may be able to prepare for the next, or even the first time it happens to you.

- Example 1: If your patient dropped of a medication and they need that medication the same day, sometimes you may not have that medication in stock. Without reading this book, you might just tell the patient "sorry ma'am, but we don't have this in stock." That patient would then proceed to ask you a series of questions like, "When can you get it by?" or "Does any other pharmacy have it?" But if you anticipate these questions before they ask, it shows the patient you care, and that you realize how important it is for them to get the medication they need as soon as they need it.

- Example 2: Some prescriptions need a prior authorization before the medication can be dispensed. So, instead of just telling the patient "Sir, your prescription needs a PA," You can first ask the patient if they've ever heard of a PA, then respond accordingly with either an explanation of it, or if they've heard of it, tell them you've already started the process.

Now these are just a few examples, but again, with experience you'll begin to notice the common situations that arise and you'll be able to start anticipating their questions by presenting solutions off the bat.

Send them Away

This one of all is going to seem a little counterintuitive, but one of the ways I've found that you can build trust and a lasting relationship with your patient is to send them away. I know your initial response to that is: what? Send them away? Yes. Here's what I mean. If you know that a patient may benefit by buying a specific product or a service somewhere else, especially if it's just one item, just tell them about it. Tell them the pharmacy next door has a really good blood pressure machine they should try. Doing this builds so much trust with a patient you wouldn't imagine. They'll forever know that whatever comes out of your mouth will always be in their best interest. Try it!

Counseling

Counseling patients on their medication is a very important part of what we do. But how do you know what concerns to tell to a patient? We already know there are so many side effects that occur with any given medication. But patients will often ask you: "are there any side effects?" Like, come on! There are tons! But, for obvious reasons, you don't want to say that to the patient. So what do you do? First, you need to know that patient may likely go home and Google all the side-effects you didn't mention, but that's ok. Explain to them you didn't mention EVERY side effect because they're usually rare. So what do you mention? I would mention the super common side effects, if you can. Maybe list the ones that are drug class specific. You can even take a peek at the other medications they're using, and if they're taking Ambien for example, and they're currently picking up tramadol, you could mention the potential increased drowsiness. Honestly, you're never going to be able to completely prepare every one of your patients for every single side effect, but touch on the most common ones, or the ones most likely to happen to them. Just do your best, and everyone will be able to live just fine with the results.

Easy Open Caps

Your prescription bottle caps are super important. The safety caps are there to prevent children from taking medications that can harm them. I'm so lucky this has never happened, but I don't know if I'd be able to live with myself knowing I mistakenly dispensed a prescription with a non-safety cap and a child ended up taking a medication that caused serious bodily harm. But what I think is often over looked is the importance of non-safety caps. By not using non-safety caps, we can physically hinder patients from taking their medications. Some of our patients live alone and can have severe dexterity issues. Many even have limited access to transportation. So imagine an elderly patient getting home to realize he or she can't even open any of their medications. Or think about the patient with serious dexterity issues due to their rheumatoid arthritis. I've dealt with both of these types of patients and I couldn't tell you how much my heart hurts hearing someone tell me they couldn't open their bottle.

You may find yourself in a situation where the prescription you're dispensing to a patient must remain in the stock bottle it comes in. But, here's a curve ball, the patient needs a non-safety cap due to their dexterity issues. And that particular bottle does not come with its own non-safety cap.

So what do you do? There are three options:

1. You can use the tool that turns child proof caps into non-safety caps to convert the stock bottle cap (Most difficult method, it's not easy!)
2. You could replace stock bottle cap with one of your vial caps.
3. Or, and this one is my personal favorite, you can find a stock bottle with an easy open cap that fits the bottle you need to dispense and just switch it out.

Voila! You can now dispense your stock bottle with a non-safety cap! Really wish someone would have told me about this right when I started, I think I went two years using that stupid tool.

Bonus Tips

Patients and Missed Doses
Don't underestimate how seriously patients view not missing their medications. I have a few patients that miss doses all the time. But I also have some that are complete adherence ninjas and never miss a dose. We know that missing a statin dose likely will have zero effects on a patient. But some don't see it this way. I have patients who swear they'll have a heart attack if they miss a dose of their simvastatin. I've found out the hard way that trying to explain steady state to a patient and tell them they'll be fine with missing a dose is not a good idea; they'll think you don't care about them and that could ruin your relationship with the patient.

Your Special Patients
Every pharmacy has their "special" patients. Sometimes when you start at a pharmacy the team will warn you about them. Or, over time you'll just start to figure them out on your own. These are the patients that likely will need more attention than most for whatever reason it may be. Sometimes, it's due to diagnosable medical issue, but sometimes it's just their personality. Whatever the cause, embrace it and just do what it takes to get them in and out of the pharmacy as quickly as possible. In my opinion, trying to treat these special patients like everyone else usually makes for a much harder day.

My injection Technique: The Icy Hot Shot
I don't mean to brag, but I provide my patients with an amazing experience when they get a vaccine with me. Not only am I personable, my injection technique is on point (pun intended). I often have patients praise how they didn't

feel a thing, and often have many patients coming back for their other vaccine needs. But why? What is it about my technique? Well, I like to think of it as special. I call it the Icy Hot Shot. I got the idea of my injection technique when I learned about why Icy Hot is such an effective product. See, with Icy Hot, its active ingredients work to essentially burn the skin providing a cooling/ heating effect. This effect on the skin serves actually as a distraction. Your brain is basically distracted by the burning reactions on your skin by the Icy Hot and it doesn't process the pain from the site of actual injury as much as if that sensation wasn't there.

Applying this theory to my intramuscular injection technique, I began using my free hand's pointer finger and thumb to create a point of contact directly above and below where I inject with my other hand. So I'm basically forming the letter C with my pointer finger and thumb using my free hand. I then apply pressure on the patient's arm with the two tips of that "C," leading with the pointiest part of my nails. Then right after that, holding the syringe like a professional dart player, with two fingers and a thumb, and then inject needle into the muscle. They never feel the needle even going in. I then release the pressure I was applying and use that free hand to the grab the body of the syringe so I can properly use my injecting hand to inject the solution with the plunger of the syringe. That's usually when they start to feel something, when the solution begins to be injected. After I inject the solution, I then reapply my C on the skin to remove the needle from the muscle. What I've learned is that the pressures of the two points of the C really take away from the point of contact with the needle and the patients skin/muscle. I'll have a whole video of this on

YouTube I promise, send me an email to Richard@RxRadio.fm, if you can't find it and I'll send you the link.

Lightening Round

- Practice good hand hygiene by not touching your patient's cellphones, you're going to have multiple patients try to hand you theirs on a daily basis.
- Try not to keep your patient's insurance cards, you'll forget to give it to them and before you know it you have a stack of insurance cards. When they hand it to you, enter the information, or make a copy of it, and hand it back to them.
- You can see your ears but you can't see your eyes. This riddle is important because it helps us remember that you can use eye drops in the ears, but you can't use ear drops in the eyes. Otic drops are expensive and some insurance companies don't even cover them. In addition, these high priced items are likely not stocked (because you read my inventory chapter). So why not have the prescriber changes it to eye drops? It's cheaper, it works, and you'll likely have it in stock.
- Don't mix or compound medications, e.g. liquid antibiotics, until your patient gets there. Last thing you want to do is damage out an unusable compound a patient never picked up.

Patients and Their Copays

Being a pharmacist in Miami, I have dealt with many different variations of people from all types of ethnic backgrounds and all types of socioeconomic status. I've had patients who've not been able to afford their $5 monthly copay, to patients who regularly pay $1,500 per month for one medication. I've had patients who are homeless to patients who own private jets. However, no matter what their particular circumstances, a lot of my patients have something in common, or have the same concern, and that's, "How much does it cost?" Not all of them care about the price. But some, no matter their socioeconomic status will be overly concerned about how much they have to pay for their prescription. Understanding that one potential commonality between all kinds of patients, you should always take the approach of price being something that is important to your patient. If you do, even if they don't care about the price, they'll really appreciate your concern.

So, what's the best way to deal with situations where cost is an issue for your patient? The first thing you'll want to do is set a threshold in your mind where if the cost of a medication is a certain price, you'll take some sort of action. For example, saw we set that threshold at $100. If anytime you get a prescription that is $100 or less, you would just fill it. But if that medication is over $100, you'd make it a point to call that particular patient and explain what their copay is and if they're ok with filling it. Tailor this number to your particular demographic. Sometimes you'll begin to just know your patients and you'll be able to catch that Ms. Smith is definitely not paying $20 copay.

Some pharmacy computer systems do this for you, they won't even let you fill a prescription until some action is taken and documented.

So, you now have to have the conversation with a patient about their high copay. Don't take this lightly because this conversation is an opportunity for you to build a good rapport with your patient. One thing I've realized that really works with talking to a patient about the high price of a medications is always prefacing the conversation with, "wow, this is expensive." By acknowledging your view as the medication being expensive, it helps demonstrate empathy and allows the patient to see you as being on their side. This makes the conversation a lot easier because they think you have their best interest in mind and value their financial situation, whatever it may be. So, when this happens, here's what I usually do. I first check to see if the patient has paid that copay before. If they're used to paying $150 every month, there's no need to take action and you can just process the prescription. But you see this is the first time they're taking this medication. I usually call the patient to let them know because if you remember our inventory management best practices, the last thing I want to do is have a prescription filled for a patient who won't come and pick it up due to its high copay. Here's how I start the conversation, "Hey Sandra, I'm giving you a call today because we were getting your medication ready for you and I noticed it was really expensive and I'm not sure if you'll be ok with this price." Almost always they'll ask for the cost right away. Then after telling them the cost, you can then start to problem solve on what to do next.

Dealing with Conflict

One things I can guarantee you'll encounter working at a pharmacy is an unhappy customer. And dealing with an angry customer is not something we're taught in school. And while some of you may be working in a retail environment, when it comes to pharmacy, the concept of "the customer is always right," doesn't always fly. Not only are we dealing with people's health, we're also having to adhere to some pretty strict laws. Buying a prescription medication is not the same as buying deodorant.

Let's start by first talking about how to prevent conflict in the first place. Usually over-communicating with a patient leads to less conflict. As soon as you see a problem, call the patient and let them know. Another way to prevent conflict is by documenting everything you do. That way, if your colleague is dealing with a patient the next day and you're not there, everything that happened will be documented, allowing you to properly communicate the right information and prevent conflict.

Back in my days at Target Pharmacy, I was able to meet with a regional manager who gave me a solid piece of advice on dealing with customers in a retail setting. He said the key to dealing with an upset customer is by trying to frame the scenario as "you and the patient" versus "the machine." Yup! He basically said he encourages us to handle situation where it's the customer versus Target the machine, and we're on the patient's side. What's crazy about this is that it was coming from a guy from corporate. He gave a few tactics which I'll share.

Get On Their Side

His first tactic for getting patients to see you're on their side was to literally get on their side. Like, get on the other side of the counter. While this may not seem practical for every upset customer, but let me tell you, it works! Maybe keep this trick in your pocket for the really upset patient, when other attempts to calm the situation have failed. But going on the other side of the counter makes patients feel like now it's the both of you against the situation, against the "machine". Whether it's something the pharmacy did, or your corporation did, of even something their doctor did. Get on their side, both physically and theoretically.

The System

In addition to getting on their side, he advised to talk about the limitations of the computer system. This comes in handy if you're in a situation where a patient is trying to have their controlled medication filled too early. You can tell the patient, "my computer system will not allow me to process this, unfortunately there's nothing I can do." I've used this quite frequently and it works really well. The patient is seeing that I'm with them in trying to get them what they want, but my computer system just won't allow me to actually do it.

Bonus Tip

Patients misplace their medications all the time. But they'll often call you before even looking for it. They'll swear they never got it. And when I was a new grad I used to believe them. I've spent precious time searching my waiting bins, checking for return to stock bottles, double checking to see if they even signed for the prescription the day the system says they picked it up; all this only for them to say soon after, "never mind I found it." Ugh, super frustrating. After the 20th time this happened to me, I stopped believing them. Now, when a patient tells me they can't find their medication, but the system says they got it, I tell them they need to look one more time. And if they say they did, I then begin to explain how I need to go look at the pharmacy's cameras to see when they were in here, get in touch with our FBI correspondent, and let them know our attorney will be reaching out. Just kidding. I do tell them I have to look at the cameras though. Nine times out of 10 I get a call within the hour where the patient tells me they found it and how tricky their couch can be. Now you could always do some minor troubleshooting, check to see if it is in fact still in your bin. But, don't spend too much time on it until more than 12 hours has passed and the patient still can't find it.

Dealing with Controls

This can be a very tricky subject. And honestly, there are so many things to consider such as federal laws, state laws, your pharmacy's policy and procedures, and even personal judgment. And due to these factors I won't really go into it here, but instead just say, always keep your patient's safety and the integrity of your license in mind. I included this not so helpful section because I didn't want you to think I forgot about it or didn't think it was important, because it is, especially with the current opioid crisis going on.

Chapter 6 – Others

Dealing with Store Managers

Depending on your type of pharmacy, you may also have a store manager to work with, or even report to. Sometimes this won't have any effect on your daily life, but sometimes store managers like to have an influence on the pharmacy, which is fair. After all, your sales do account for the overall store sales. Only problem is, a lot of times these store managers are not healthcare professionals, let alone pharmacists. So a lot of the direction you may get from a store manager may seem out of touch or not practical. One thing that worked for me was trying to connect with them. Like my patients, I would ask questions to see if I could find something in common with them. This really helped aid in relationship building which made communication with them stronger. When you develop a good relationship with these leaders you can then have meaningful conversations around both of your goals and what you both can be doing to achieve them. However, the reality is some store managers may be receptive to learning more about what you do, leading to a healthy relationship, but some may not.

Dealing with Prescribers

One of the toughest parts of the job as a community pharmacist is dealing with prescribers. And I say tough not at the level of difficulty, but more so the level of frustration. I feel like the majority of my day at the pharmacy is spent dealing with a prescriber's office. What doesn't help is that when you're dealing with these offices you may not even be dealing with a healthcare professional. It's so challenging and can be an extremely frustrating experience.

You're just trying to get the patient their medication yet you are met with so much uncertainty and often even aggression to your questions of the prescription. These experiences are usually more frustrating as a new grad because you're overly concerned with everything and may find yourself calling on more things than the veteran pharmacist. I hope this section will help get you through your first couple months. But before we get on to some tips, whenever you are dealing with a prescriber's office, document everything. Who you spoke with, what they told you and consider recording the time you spoke to that person. Here are some tips:

Get Help from the Patient
I usually like to involve the patient in the process of getting something verified for a few reasons. First, I'd like them to see that it's not easy to just call and talk directly with the prescriber or get the answers you need within a minute or two. Plus, if a doctor's office is getting a call from both the pharmacy and the prescriber, I've noticed they tend to do things a lot quicker.

Guide Them
When dealing with a doctor's office, a lot of times you have to guide them towards the right answer; especially if we're dealing with a simple clarification like a missing quantity.

Most of the time we know what the prescription should say, we're just calling to cover our bases and document. They'll often get angry at us for trying to get a full coherent prescription. I know right, how dare they?

You'll often never speak with the prescriber. But with all of this, the thing to always keep in mind is that the most important thing is the safety of the patient. So if you're dealing with some issue that really just doesn't seem right and you can't speak directly with the prescriber that should be a legit red flag you shouldn't fill it. Always look out for the patient's safety, and then make sure to protect yourself and your license.

Know Your Stuff
Sometimes you'll have the true honor of actually speaking with the prescriber. And you'll then have the opportunity to make a change on the prescription. If it's a clinical recommendation, make sure to have some reasoning for a clinical decision. Be ready for some dialogue. But also be open to feedback, while we're medication experts, you'll still learn a lot from prescribers. Some prescribers will be jerks and some will seem like they're that best friend from high school you haven't spoken to in a while but always hit it off when you reconnect. Either way, all dialogue should include your reasoning for alternatives with keeping the patient in mind. Sometimes you'll win some and sometimes you'll lose some. But again, always document everything.

Chapter 7 – and the Future

Feeling Fulfilled

This is a tough topic, but I really wanted to touch on it, and that's whether you can live a fulfilling career in community pharmacy. While today's landscape will point towards the answer no, I actually do think it is possible. Work conditions have changed quite a bit. A lot of pharmacies have been cutting hours both for pharmacists and pharmacy technicians to account for an ever changing healthcare. But even in these tough times, being a community pharmacist can be extremely rewarding for all types of people. If you're the competitive type, there's plenty of metrics you can use to measure your success and gamify your day to day. Maybe you just want a job where you can show up do your thing and then leave, this lifestyle is also a possibility with community pharmacy. Most of the time, we don't take our work home. Lastly, and this one is my favorite, you get to work with people all day. If you're super passionate about relationships with patients, you'll have endless opportunities to have an impact on people's lives. Even just getting to know your team and working closely with them can make this a really great job to have. The only people I think may have a hard time here are those who want to be more of a clinical pharmacist. While I do believe you can still apply a lot of your clinical knowledge, the landscape isn't really designed for that. Clinically, you do as much as you want or as little as you want. You could take the opportunity to talk to every patient about the most common side effects, or call and try to intervene on every clinical interaction. It'll just take time. So no matter the type of person you are or hope to be, if you find yourself in a community pharmacy, you can live with a fulfilled career, or you could continuously be thinking about the future.

"Remember that you are in control of your environment. Just as a pitcher or quarterback controls the pace of play, you can control expectations and outcomes. Praise your staff, rewrite the rules for how you will practice pharmacy and integrate as much clinical knowledge into your day to day as you want or need. Community pharmacy is more than just being cheap, fast, and accurate. Be the change that you want to see. Your patients will see your level of commitment and buy into it. Keep the goal of quality care at the center of your career and you cannot go wrong." – Jim Knight, PharmD

While the main goal for this book is to prepare the community pharmacist, the profession is going to see some amazing changes and I wanted to share my thoughts on it. A lot of people are usually concerned that technology will replace pharmacists. However, the role of a pharmacist will always be needed. Until the robots actually take over, we'll always be in demand. It will be competitive and it's likely not going to look like what it does today. When we were more commonly known as the "Druggist," especially in the early 1900s late 1800s we were actually preparing and making medications. Now, with advances in tech, medicines are mass produced and we're not just making sure the patient gets the right drug; we're much more clinically involved than we used to be. So, what's to come? Well, for one, innovations in technology will dramatically change the way medications are dispensed. There'll soon be a time where after a medication is prescribed to a patient, that medication will be at the patient's door in two hours. That's just one change. How can you be ready for these changes? What if jobs do start to become harder to get? Well, I think the answer to both of these questions relies on your activity on social media.

Social Media

In 2017 I gave a talk at the UF college of Pharmacy (Go Gators) and I asked the question, "Who here is on social media?" To no one's surprise, the entire room raised their hand, except one. One person didn't raise their hand because they were eating a sandwich. But, literally everyone else raised their hand for being on social media. And I'll point out to you what I pointed out to them. That room was not an anomaly. It was a representation of all the healthcare professionals of the modern world. Whether it is on Instagram, Facebook, YouTube, Snapchat, Twitter, or Twitch, we're all on something.

It's time we start acknowledging this and taking it seriously. We shouldn't just be utilizing social media to have fun or connect with old friends and family. We need to start thinking about social media and how it could propel our careers. It's also a great source of information. If you're following leaders in your industry or in something specific you're interested in, they'll likely share innovations or trends on their platforms. It's also a great tool to demonstrate not only to other healthcare professionals, but to the world, what we do, what we're capable of, and how valuable we are as a part of the healthcare team.

Everything you do and put on social media has the potential to be seen by many, including future employers, so be careful. We're also living in a time where politics are pretty polarizing. So, if your political views supersede your job opportunities and potential reputation, by all means, speak your views. But if it does not, I would seriously discourage the use of social media to voice your political views because unfortunately, it can have a negative impact on your career as a pharmacist.

Social media has given healthcare professionals a platform to build their reputation and I really see it as a way to accelerate your career. But I really think you can create a platform or an audience around a topic and then become the expert in that one topic, whether you have residency training or not.

For example, here's how I see something playing out. Let's take transplant pharmacy, for example. You're a community pharmacist, but you've listened to the Rx Radio Podcast about transplant pharmacy and decided that's what you were born to do. You decide you need to get your foot in the door in a hospital since you have no experience. You find a hospital currently going through new leadership and manage to land a per diem position. At nights or your days off you begin researching transplant medicine. You then create a blog to start gathering your thoughts and documenting your learning from a fresh perspective, detailing your ideas for helping patients with compliance and coping with their new organs. You then start the nation's first podcast dedicated to transplant pharmacy, interviewing transplant pharmacists from across the country, or even the world. At the writing of this book, such a podcast does not exist. You then begin to wonder what it would take to start a transplant program at your institution. You hit it off really well with one of your podcast guests, who, coincidentally, has been looking to relocate to your area. You two then develop and pitch both of your new positions at your current hospital for a transplant department. Boom, it could happen. Or you could continue to do what you're doing now. It's worth a try, right?

"You are never "stuck" in a job." - Tiffany Upshaw, PharmD, BCPS

If you've bought in to the importance of social media and want to start building your brand, start with some self reflection. Do you like to be on camera? Would you rather become a content writer? Or do you prefer neither of these, but you absolutely love talking to people? Whatever it may be, start with that. Start a YouTube channel, a blog, or a podcast and then go from there. And hey, maybe your passions aren't in pharmacy. Maybe you love Disney, or playing the guitar. You can have a fulfilling life living out these passions even while being a full-time pharmacist. If you find yourself being passionate about something else, I'd highly recommend you read *Crush It,* and his follow up book, *Crushing It*, by Gary Vaynerchuk.

Let's move on to talk what's next for our industry? As you could imagine, there's many new advances in healthcare, but the following are what I'm the most excited about.

Machine Learning, Artificial Intelligence, and Voice

The power of voice and what's called machine learning is still in its infancy. 2017 was the first year people actually got Alexa devices (and the competition) as gifts. Soon, whether it is an Alexa device, Google Home, Apple Pod, or some machine that hasn't come to market yet, there will be one of these things within 5–10 feet radius of you at all times. In your bathroom, car, pharmacy etc. I just asked Siri for a calculation the other day which helped me accurately enter information for a prescription. We literally don't need to learn math anymore. So where do pharmacists fit into this? How can we use this technology to provide better care? Glad you asked. If you didn't know, there are a couple skills every successful pharmacist needs to master: The ability to ask the right questions and the ability to communicate effectively.

The unique thing about these two skills is that they're actually keys to the design of a successful voice experience. Because of this, there's a huge potential for pharmacists to have major roles in designing voice experiences around healthcare. There are already Alexa skills that could handle basic questions pharmacists encounter every day, e.g., "how do I treat allergies," or "what can I put on a burn." And it's just the beginning; soon we'll see these devices handle more complicated scenarios like post/pre op procedure questions. The more time passes the more advanced and smarter apps on these devices will get and the more it will need a highly trained individual, such as pharmacists.

Detachment of Pharmacist and Dispensing

I do foresee an unfortunate situation happening. And it happens in most industries. We saw it with Uber and the traditional taxi industry; we're seeing it with AirBnb and the traditional hotel industry. Everything traditional is being re-thought. And I think pharmacy will be no different. Once the sharing economy hits the pharmacy world, in addition to advancements in dispensing, I think there will be disruptions in the patient-pharmacist relationship. The traditional pharmacist that is tied to dispensing a medication may be a thing of the past. There will soon be a total disconnect of pharmacists and medication dispensing. Most individuals who take medications will have their own personal pharmacist to help them manage their medications and disease states. But that pharmacist will not be employed by the pharmacy that provided the medication. The job descriptions of these new roles are what I dreamed about in pharmacy school. Not being a highly paid cashier. Your role will go from occasionally ringing up Sandra's weekly loaf of bread, to designing a highly individualized medication management plan for someone taking 15 medications. It's what we actually went to school for.

Pharmacists in Primary Care

Even other healthcare providers are going to feel their roles changing. Primary care practices are becoming overwhelmed with work and we're starting to see a big shift in more and more healthcare providers relying on pharmacists for their knowledge on medications. Because of this, I see a future where pharmacists are employed at primary care practices. Actually, forget the future; it's actually already happening. Maybe you haven't heard of it yet, but I think it'll be widespread, especially with new drugs coming out every year, new findings and updates to guidelines; it only makes sense for a physician to have a pharmacist part of his/her practice. Could you imagine a world where prescriptions wouldn't even leave the doctor's office until it's reviewed by a pharmacist?!

Blockchain

Bitcoin and blockchain are some new buzzwords that were hot in late 2017, early 2018. But where does it fit into healthcare, and more so, pharmacists? The whole movement starts to apply to our field when we realize that this technology has completely revolutionized the way we store data, view currency, and utilize legal contracts. Think of Bitcoin as being the first "application" of the technology. It started off by revolutionizing traditional paper currency, but it's turning into much, much, more. Large organizations like IBM and Microsoft are already investing into the tech, and there are companies already developing blockchain healthcare applications. The two main areas of focus for blockchain in healthcare are tracking drugs during the drug supply chain and use in electronic health records. The one thing I haven't seen yet, but I could only imagine will be here one day, is the revolutionizing of sending electronic prescriptions. During the blockchain boom, there has been this thing called smart contracts utilizing a specific type of blockchain called Ethereum. Smart contracts will likely revolutionize a lot of industries, including real estate and the vehicle purchase industry, but I also think these smart contracts can be used revolutionizing the way we send a prescription. Can you imagine a time when prescriptions are sent to a pharmacy with already built in alternatives authorized by the prescriber given certain situations at the pharmacy? With a smart contract, a physician can send a prescription for penicillin, but if there is a listed allergy that contract (prescription) can be automatically changed to a recommended alternative. And guess who could be behind designing some of these algorithms? Yes, pharmacists! The tech behind it all is complicated and out of the scope of this book really, but if you're interested, start researching on that fun website we all know and love: Google.com. Any who, these new advances in technology mentioned in this chapter will all have the potential for impactful roles that pharmacists can play a part in. Our future is bright!

Outro

Hey! Woo hoo! You made it through to the end! Really hope you got some value out of the book. I always wished I had something like this when I was just starting out. Now, I feel like where I am with my experience, I've got enough years and patients screaming at me under my belt to write it. One thing to keep in mind though, is that most of what I spoke about here is rooted in my own experiences. Your experiences may be different. But, I hope this will help prepare you to be the pharmacist you always hoped you'd be.

Thanks for reading.

Take care,

Richard

About the Author

Dr. Richard Waithe received his PharmD from the University of Florida and has over 7 years of experience in community pharmacy. He's passionate about helping people better manage their health and medications. He's the Editor in Chief of Rx Radio, a media company focused on engaging and inspiring pharmacists and pharmacy students to better the profession of pharmacy. Through podcasting and producing media content for platforms like Alexa, Facebook, LinkedIn, and Medium, Rx Radio is an emerging leader and media influencer in healthcare. Although Richard currently lives in his hometown of Miami, FL, he loves to hit the slopes with his Fiancé. He snowboards, and she skis, but somehow, they've been able to make their relationship work.

Made in the USA
Columbia, SC
16 February 2019